Claytown Press
San Diego, CA 92120
www.claytownpress.com

First edition
10 9 8 7 6 5 4 3 2 1
Library of Congress Cataloging-in-Publication Data
Lekven, Shelley Daniels. 1955 -
Lily Pond / written and illustrated by Shelley Daniels Lekven. p. cm
Summary: A little girl frog daydreams about her future.
[1. Stories in rhyme. 2. Frogs-Fiction. 3. Careers-Fiction.
4. Girl Empowerment-Fiction.] I. Title.
Library of Congress Control Number: 2017952767
ISBN: 978-0-9988666-0-4

Printed in China

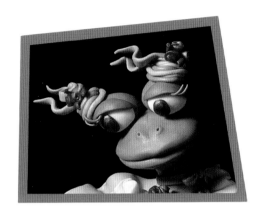

Lily Pond

To Robert,
Hayley, John & Katelyn
And to my parents
for "Claytown"

–S.D.L.

Little Lily Pond lay awake one night,

After her mother had turned out the light.

"When I grow up what will I be?

Where will I go and who will I see?

What will I look like?

I hope I look nice.

Will I be famous and president twice?

Will I build houses?

Or dance?

Sing?

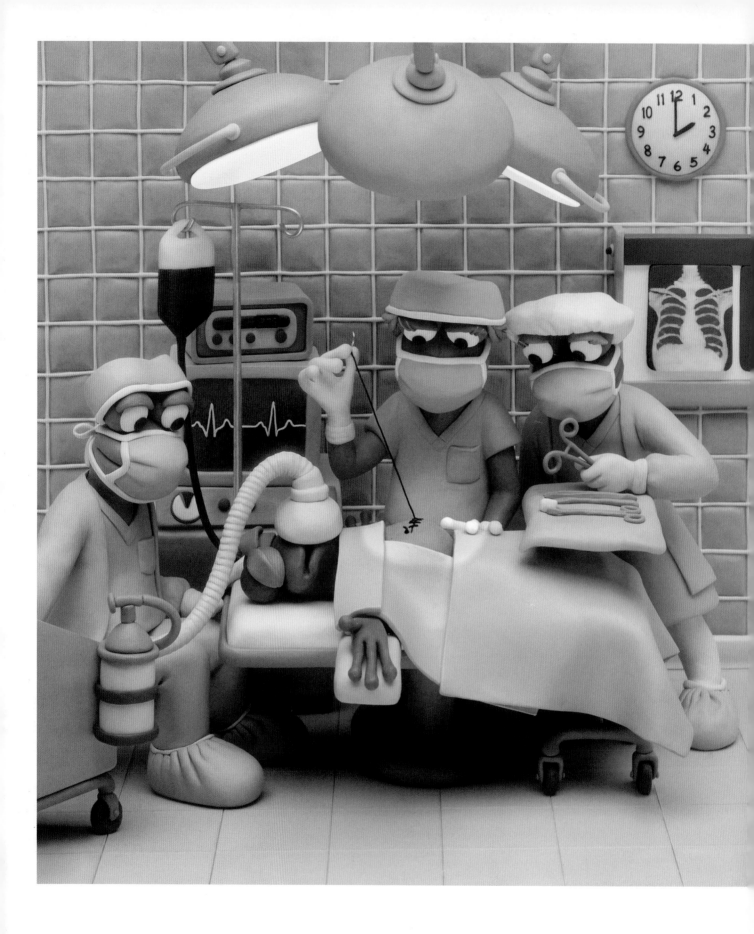

Maybe save lives?

Study science and facts?

Will I fly spaceships?

Balloons?

Or in planes?

What will things look like?

I hope not too strange.

Who might I marry?

And where are they now?

I hope that they're happy

and laughing out loud.

Will we have children named Bob, Sue and Paul?

Or will we decide

to have no kids at all?

Where will I travel and who will I meet?

A life of adventure might be kind of neat!

Will I write books about this or that trip?

Or sail on the seas as I captain a ship?

But there's time to decide. I need to sleep.

These dreams of the future will just have to keep.

Being a kid is so fun that I'm happy to wait.

I'm seven years old . . .

But tomorrow I'm eight!"

Shelley Daniels Lekven began playing with clay at the age of six when she, along with her sister, brother, and best friend, started a clay town on the dining room table with some old balls of modeling clay.

Her parents, remarkably, let it stay. "Claytown" thrived and grew to become the centerpiece of their childhoods for ten wonderful years.

Shelley became a 3D artist and was a character sculptor on *The Nightmare Before Christmas, Toy Story* and *James & the Giant Peach*. She worked on the illustrations for <u>Lily Pond</u> in her spare time.

The scenes were sculpted from soft, colored modeling clay. Skies were added later by computer.

Shelley Daniels Lekven lives in San Diego, California with her husband and three children (all of whom would rather draw than sculpt).

More at: <u>www.lilypondbook.com</u>

Photographers:

Hans Wendt
Tony Garcia
Michael Marzelli
Jim Coit

Image Editor:

Gary Karsten